THE GIRLS

THE GIRLS

BY FRANKLIN FOLGER

Doubleday & Company, Inc.
Garden City, New York

PREFACE

What kind of man could draw a cartoon like THE GIRLS and make his ladies so charming, engaging, and winsome—six days a week?

Only a bachelor, of course.

Franklin Folger doesn't have to answer for his humor to a wife, or, even more important, to a mother-in-law. But if he did, it is doubtful that even those severe critics could find fault with THE GIRLS. For Folger has never been scornful or maliciously unkind in his humorous panel. "People were not meant to be hurt," was his comment when one of his fans observed that he never offended anyone. That feeling probably explains why Folger's gentle spoofing of women of all ages has endeared him to millions of newspaper readers.

A native of Cincinnati, Franklin Folger studied painting, commercial art, and cartooning at the Cincinnati Art Academy. Before he conceived the idea of THE GIRLS, he was a free-lance cartoonist and illustrator, and his work appeared in *This Week, Ladies' Home Journal, Saturday Evening Post,* and many other magazines. Far from relaxing after creating his weekly six cartoons, he continues to produce and sell a dozen or so cartoons a week. His "free time" is a myth.

THE GIRLS is distributed by the Sun-Times Daily News Syndicate and appears in well over a hundred newspapers throughout the country. It is difficult to tell whether Folger's humor appeals more to his male or female audience, because fan mail pours in from both sexes. We hope this little book will please "old" readers and introduce new ones to Folger's refreshing, nostalgic, and plausible humor.

THE GIRLS

"What are their names?"

"You could use a trim."

"No, thank you, just looking."

"But now it is time to welcome summer, so, hello,
summer! Hello, Summer! HELLO, SUMMER!"

"How do you get it through the little hole?"

"Charles: Had to run over to Harriet's for a few minutes—door key is under mat on porch."

"Forgot my blue."

"But, Harriet, if you've definitely decided to overthrow the Cuban government, won't you need help?"

"Gorgeous, beautiful, doll face—why, no, I wouldn't
say you had the wrong number."

18

"Everybody's so friendly in this town!"

"No, dear, you should say, 'I saw the kitchen stool'—
not, 'I sawed the kitchen stool.' "

"Please, girls! There are lots of other jobs to do!"

23

"I've never felt so relieved. I was afraid he'd just
fiddle with something and it would start."

"Give the ball to the man, dear—we thought we'd
save you the trouble of having to walk after it."

"I simply love this coat—would you have it in a wool
with long lapels, a different color, buttons,
and a belt?"

"I've reached the age where no matter how much
time I spend at the beauty parlor, I come away
looking like I haven't been waited on."

"Why, Mr. Johnson! So you were the tiny leaf
floating around in my cup of tea."

"I'd just like to see you love MY neighbors."

"And these two pieces must be squeezed gently in
rich suds and then rinsed and the water gradually
pressed out. Be sure not to twist or wring——"

31

"My doctor allows me only 1200 calories a day, but
it isn't so hard because I have two other doctors
who allow me the same number."

"*Just look at that, will you—that fool man driving that close ahead of me!*"

"Mrs. Webster is our only speaker today. The rest of
the program is entertainment."

"Instead of all huddling together in town, you'd think they'd build service stations out where you need them."

"Did you ever think what kind of a duck dinner you could get for $59.95?"

"Harriet, couldn't we just stay home this summer?"

"The police were just wonderful about it. One of them asked me if I'd like for the city to remove all the lampposts."

"It's agreed then—present committee heads are to
be re-elected since there's no sense in wasting all
that stationery with their names on it."

40

"Come inside, boys and girls—I've arranged a little
get-together!"

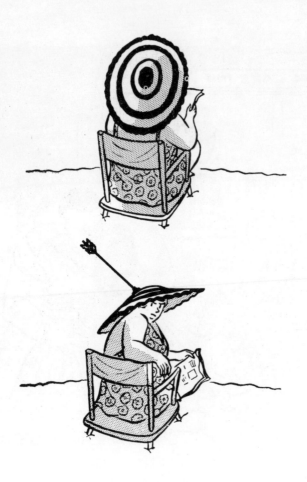

"Where in the world do you meet those silly women
you write about?"

43

"*I don't care what your speedometer says—when I go over 50 my hat flies off.*"

"But I WON'T hippity-hop!"

"You don't think it makes me look TOO dangerous,
do you?"

"Oh, all right—— GOOD MORNING, BIRDS!"

"That's more like it."

"Now, who would like to go to the flower show?"

"Today we visit Holland."

"That's funny, at home he won't touch French-fries."

"Guess what, my roses won!"

"Does anybody here own the car with the license
number M-901-69?"

"I don't see anything so wonderful about his plays.
The only thing he's done is assemble a lot of old,
familiar quotations."

"Have you anything left would be more like it."

"I'm not lost—I just found a street I don't know!"

"——and shortly after Christmas the Websters, next door, had a baby—and then late in January my grandson visited me. Last month we had the house painted——"

"And then I signaled VERY CLEARLY that I had changed my mind."

"Cats sprung at me."

"Young lady, it is of no concern to me whether or not
it's kissproof!"

"Mr. Johnson! We're dueling over you!"

"HI, BEAUTIFUL!"

"If you ask me, the prettiest flower in Madam's
garden will be Madam."

"Just wait until mother gets you home."

"How do you know when you're finished?"

"Forget it, lady."

"Coffee's weak—awful drapes—ham's salty—cold in
here—coffee's weak—awful—"

"Five sixty-nine—what did you get?"

"I'm going to count three once more and then I'm going to sit down. I'm not kidding this time!"

"Can't I be mysterious and still see where
I'm going?"

"MAYBE IF YOU'D JIGGLE IT!"

"I want some of those stocks that skyrocket!"

"I might know you'd get seats like these—we're
going to be the last ones out of here!"

"Is the regular man off today?"

"Charles, I let him chase me all the way from town.
I thought you'd know better what to say to him!"

"Do you have a gift that doesn't look like it was
purchased in a railroad station?"

"Just what is it you CAN'T tell the players without
a score card?"

"And in here, folks, is the semi-private bath.
Thank you, Mr. Krebs."

*"Oh, I had looked forward to your bringing
little Bobby."*

"Oh, dear, all I can remember is Rule 5—
disperse the crowd."

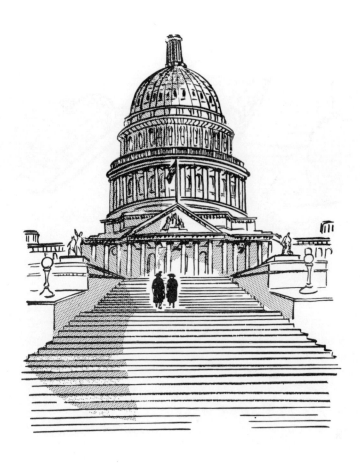

*"Goodness! If they have to walk up these every day,
it's no wonder they never do anything."*

"Now remember, young man, no stunting!"

"And if he doesn't come out from under the piano and give me my magazine immediately, you'll be right over? Thank you, MR. DOG CATCHER."

"There aren't any young pretty ones, I notice."

"Perhaps I'd better tell it over again."

"Which one was it that was so witty on television?"

"MAKE EDNA STOP!"

"*Bless their hearts. I bet their mothers are glad to hear their voices.*"

"Charles is busy right now. He's getting ready to go
to the symphony with me."

"Just ME, Mother."

93

"Please, Mrs. Mayer, you've just been poisoned—
you're dying—put a little life into it!"

"Now, five letters across meaning:
Mediterranean shrub."

"Oh, heavens! The note to the milkman!"